MUSIC WORKOUT

Grade 6

Jean Archibald and Bernadette Marmion

Royal Irish Academy of Music

GRADE 6
Syllabus

Time Signatures All simple and compound times and the irregular time signatures of $\frac{5}{4}$ $\frac{5}{8}$ $\frac{7}{4}$ $\frac{7}{8}$.

Clefs The addition of the Tenor (C) clef. Transposing a melody up or down an octave between any of the four clefs.

Keys Scales, key signatures and tonic triads with their inversions of major keys up to 7 sharps and flats and both forms of minor scales up to 5 sharps and flats.

Intervals / Transposition All intervals not greater than an octave and the inversion of intervals. Transposing a melody either up or down by any of the following intervals : major 2nd, major or minor 3rd, perfect 4th or 5th. The melody will be in a major or minor key, using only treble or bass clef and will include some chromatic notes.

Triads / 4 part Chords
a Construction of major, minor, diminished and augmented triads in root position on any note.
b The writing of the following triads in keys appropriate to the grade:
(i) tonic triads in root position, 1st inversion, and 2nd inversion;
(ii) subdominant and dominant triads in root position only.
c Arranging the primary triads (tonic, subdominant and dominant) as four part chords (root position) for S.A.T. B.
d The writing in open score (using treble and bass clefs) of a passage for S.A.T. B. written in short score, or vice versa.
e The identification of the primary chords (root position) in an extract scored for piano, voices or string quartet.

Composition To compose a melody from a given opening to make a total of 8 bars. Marks of tempo, phrasing and expression to be added to the completed melody. Writing a rhythm to words using $\frac{2}{4}$ $\frac{3}{4}$ $\frac{4}{4}$ and $\frac{6}{8}$ times.

Observation General questions on a musical extract to include the identification of ornaments.

History / Instruments A general knowledge of the Baroque period to include style, forms, main composers and their standard works.
Terms indicating special effects on instruments.
Transposing instruments.

A Note to the Teacher
Text Signals

● indicates where new concepts and information are introduced.

■ indicates suggestions, points to be memorised and useful hints.

CONTENTS

Part 1

1 Major Scales - F♯ and C♯
2 Major Scales - G♭ and C♭
3 Sight Clapping 1 : Revision
4 Revision : Time Signatures / Grouping
5 Exercises on Time and Grouping
6 Measuring Intervals
7 Measuring Intervals Downwards
8 Singing with Solfa 1

9 Singing with Solfa 2
10 The C Clef : Tenor Stave
11 Triad Inversion
12-13 Word Rhythm : 4-line Stanzas
14 Word Rhythm : 4-line Stanzas: Exercises
15 General Observation 1
16 Test 1

Part 2

17 Transcribing to the Tenor Stave
18 Two New Minor Keys - G♯ and B♭
19 A Page of Minor Scales
20 Irregular Time Signatures : $\frac{5}{4}$ $\frac{5}{8}$ $\frac{7}{4}$ $\frac{7}{8}$
21 Irregular Time : More Exercises
22 Inversion of Intervals
23 Inversion of Intervals : Exercises
24 Sight Clapping 2

25 Triads : Close / Open Position
26 Transposition : Major Keys
27 Singing with Solfa 3 : Leaps to d
28 Completing 8-bar Melodies
29 8-Bar Melody Exercises
30 The Baroque Period
31 General Observation 2
32 Test 2

Part 3

33 Octave Transposition with C Clef
34 Primary Triads : Major Keys
35 Primary Triads : Minor Keys
36 Sight Clapping 3
37 Transposition with Chromatic Notes
38 Transposition : Minor Keys
39 Minor Key Transposition : Exercises

40 Singing with Solfa 4 : Leaps to l (minor)
41 Word Rhythm $\frac{6}{8}$
42 Arranging Chords for Voices
43 Arranging Chords for Voices : Exercises
44 General Observation 3
45 Test 3

Part 4

46 SATB : Primary Chords in Major Keys
47 SATB : Primary Chord Ex. Major Keys
48 SATB : Primary Chords in Minor Keys
49 Recognising SATB Chords : Major / Minor
50 Transposing Instruments
51 Transposing Instruments : Exercises
52 Singing with Solfa 5 : Leaps to t and si
53 Melody Writing : More Exercises
54 Short Score / Open Score
55 Short Score / Open Score : Exercises
56 Identifying Primary Chords : Piano Music

57 Identify Primary Chords(piano) : Exercises
58 Identify Primary Chords : String Quartets
59 Ornaments
60 More about Word Rhythms
61 Word Rhythm : Exercises
62 Augmented and Diminished Triads
63 Sight Clapping 4 : Syncopation / Jazz Rhythm
64 Instruments and Special Effects
65 General Observation 4
66 Test 4

Part 5

67 Aural / Visual Observation : Introduction
68-71 Aural / Visual Observation : Exercises

72-74 Revision Tests A - C
75 Key Signatures : Tables

First published in 2000 by
The Royal Irish Academy of Music
Westland Row, Dublin 2.

©2000 by The Royal Irish Academy of Music

ISBN   1 - 902140 - 07 - 9

Music processing   Jean Archibald and Bernadette Marmion
Typesetting and graphics   Creighton Music, Dublin 14.
Cover design   Origin Design Associates.
Printed by   Brunswick Press, Dublin 12.

PART 1
F# and C# MAJOR SCALES

■ Before you study this page, refer to page 75 at the end of the book to make sure you know the key signatures of the sharp major keys: G D A E and B.

● You remember that each new sharp major scale begins on the <u>5th</u> note of the preceding scale, so by counting up a perfect 5th from the tonic of the last scale you studied (B major), you arrive at F#, the tonic of the next scale. To get the next scale after F#, you count up a further perfect 5th to C#.

As with all sharp major scales, each new scale must include all the sharps from the preceding scale. A new sharp is then added to the 7th note, the leading note.

These are the key signatures and tonic triads of the two new scales. Notice the shape of the key signatures.

■ As every note has now been sharpened, there are no further sharp major keys.

Exercise 1 Add the clef and the key signature or accidentals as directed to make these scales. Mark the semitones. Write the tonic triads using accidentals.

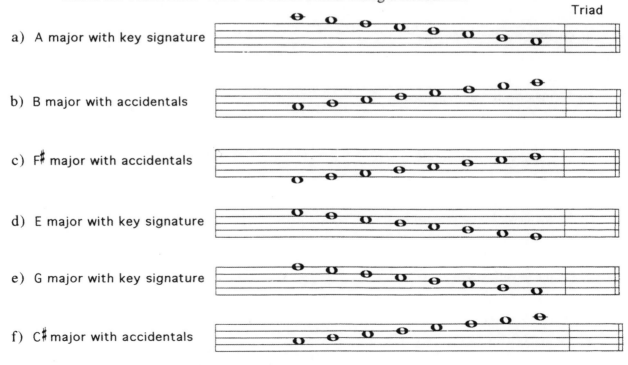

Gb and Cb MAJOR SCALES

This page revises the flat major scales studied in Grade 5: F Bb Eb Ab and Db. Two new scales are now added. If necessary, refer to page 75 to revise what you know about the flat key signatures.

Each new flat major scale begins on the <u>4th</u> note of the preceding scale, so by counting up a perfect 4th from the tonic of the last scale you studied (Db), you arrive at Gb, the tonic of the next scale. To get the next scale after Gb, you count up a further perfect 4th to Cb.

As with all flat major scales, each new scale must include all the flats from the preceding scale. A new flat is then added to the 4th note, the subdominant.

These are the key signatures and tonic triads of the two new scales. Notice the shape of the key signatures.

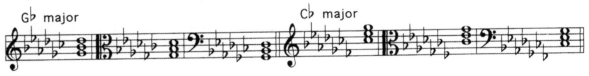

■ As every note has now been flattened, there are no further flat major keys.

Exercise 2 Add the clef and the key signature or accidentals as directed to make these scales. Mark the semitones. Write the tonic triads using accidentals.

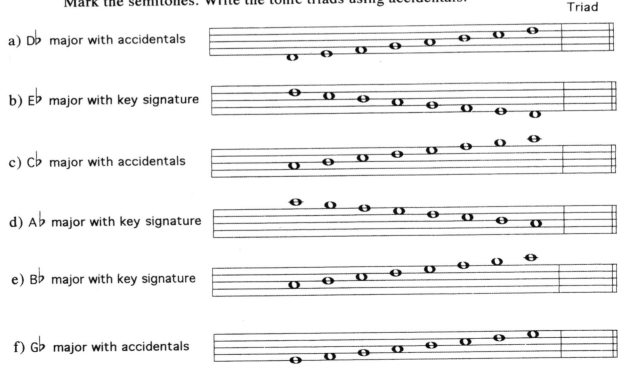

3

■ Use these tables to revise the rhythm patterns you learnt in Grade 5.

1 Any pattern causing difficulty should be paired with another easier one, to help make it secure.

2 In the Compound Table practise clapping in $\frac{9}{8}$ by adding another beat group or add two more groups for $\frac{12}{8}$.

3 When practising, always be sure to maintain a steady beat.

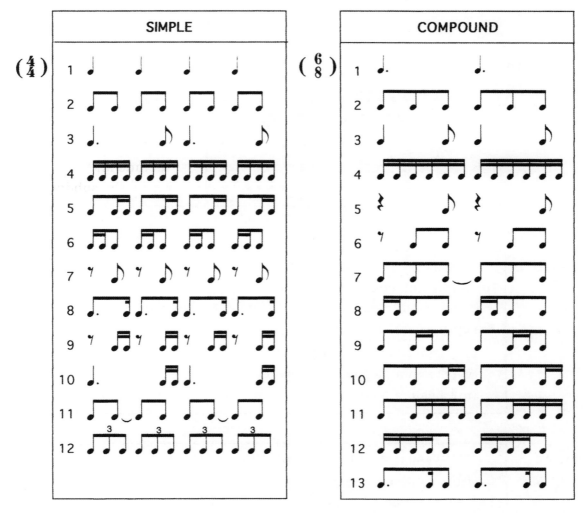

Exercise 3 Practise clapping the patterns in each table in different ways by: (i) varying the order ; (ii) clapping as a duet or a round with one or more people.

Exercise 4 Clap each of the following rhythms.

REVISION of TIME SIGNATURES and GROUPING

■ This page revises time signatures and the grouping (beaming) of notes.

Revision 1 Enter the time signature numbers in each grid. The first one has been filled.

SIMPLE

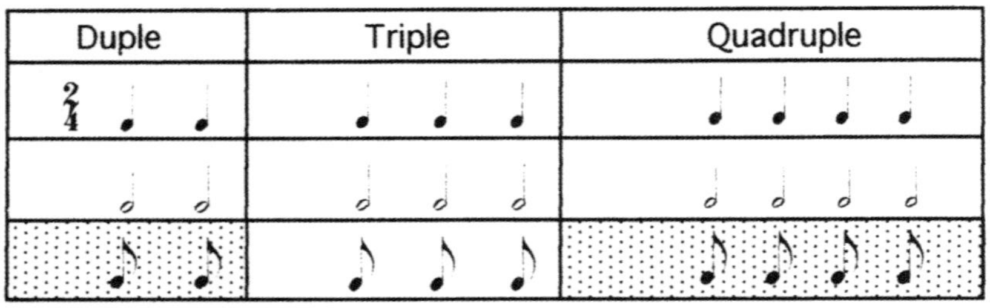

	Duple	Triple	Quadruple
$\frac{2}{4}$			

COMPOUND

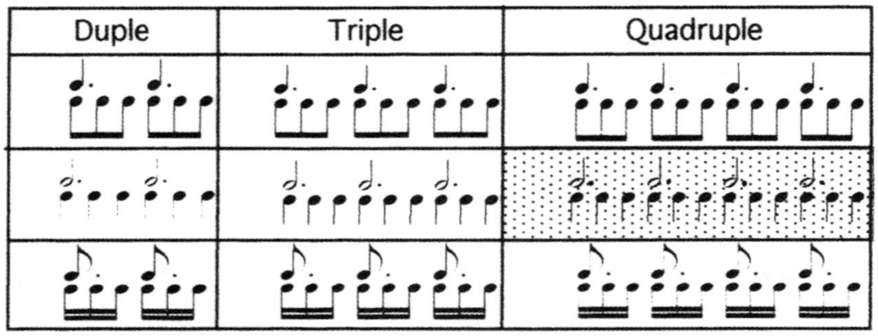

	Duple	Triple	Quadruple

Time signatures in greyed boxes are very seldom used.

Revision 2

SUMMARY of POINTS on GROUPING (beaming) NOTES

In simple and compound times :

Beam enough quavers / semiquavers to make up <u>single</u> beats.

Exceptions in simple time:

In $\frac{2}{4}$ and $\frac{3}{4}$ beam a <u>whole</u> bar of quavers.

In $\frac{4}{4}$ beam a <u>half</u> bar of quavers.

In $\frac{3}{8}$ beam a <u>whole</u> bar of quavers/semiquavers.

Revision 3

SUMMARY of POINTS on WRITING RESTS

1 Use a semibreve rest for a <u>whole</u> bar's rest.
2 A separate beat normally needs a separate rest.
3 Complete an incomplete beat by adding rests in easy stages.
4 Use separate rests for <u>parts</u> 2 and 3 of compound beats.

Exception : Use one rest for a <u>half</u> bar in quadruple time.

● **Irregular groups**

In simple times a plain beat may be broken into irregular groups of 3, 5 or 7 equal parts as follows :

Similarly in compound times, the dotted beat may also be subdivided irregularly. Some of the groups most often used are :

EXERCISES on TIME and GROUPING

Exercise 5   Group (beam) these rhythms to suit each of the given time signatures.

$\frac{3}{4}$ _____

$\frac{6}{8}$ _____

Exercise 6   Write a 3-bar rhythm in each of these times. Use a mixture of notes and rests and include the rhythms already written in some bars. Group with care.

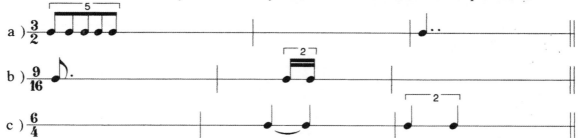

a) $\frac{3}{2}$

b) $\frac{9}{16}$

c) $\frac{6}{4}$

Exercise 7   Rewrite the following extract in compound time but keep the effect the same.

Schubert. Op.94

Exercise 8   Complete each bar by adding the missing rest/s at * .

Beethoven. pf sonata Op. 110

Exercise 9   Without changing the order of the notes, make any necessary adjustments to each of these rhythms to show correct grouping for the new time signature.

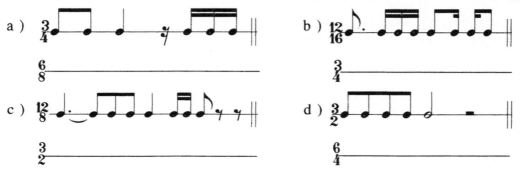

a) $\frac{3}{4}$ b) $\frac{12}{16}$

$\frac{6}{8}$ $\frac{3}{4}$

c) $\frac{12}{8}$ d) $\frac{3}{2}$

$\frac{3}{2}$ $\frac{6}{4}$

Exercise 10   Add bar lines in the following extracts.

Chopin. Nocturne Op.15

a)

Beethoven. Symphony No.1

b)

MEASURING INTERVALS

■ Revise the following ideas about intervals.

Standard intervals   These are formed from the tonic of a major scale. They are:

Major 2nd 3rd 6th 7th   Perfect 4th 5th 8th

The quality of all other intervals depends on increases or reductions of these.

Numerical value   This is the number of letter names between the lower and upper notes including both these notes, e.g. 3rd, 5th, etc.

Quality name   This indicates the type of interval, i.e. whether it is major, minor, perfect, augmented, or diminished.

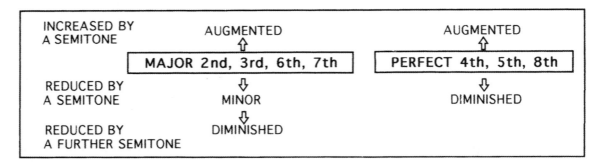

● Another way to find the quality names of <u>small</u> intervals is to learn how many tones and semitones each interval contains.

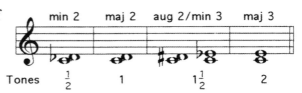

To measure perfect 4ths and 5ths, follow this rule keeping the keyboard in mind.

■ | Except when using F and B together   **White** goes to **White**   **Black** goes to **Black** |

Exercise 11   Describe these intervals.

Exercise 12   Draw these intervals above the given notes.

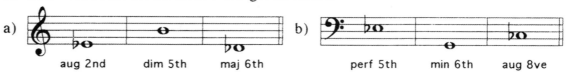

Exercise 13   Name the bracketed intervals in this melody.

● **MEASURING INTERVALS DOWNWARDS**

While it is common to measure intervals <u>upwards</u> from the <u>lower</u> note, it is also useful to be able to measure them <u>downwards</u> from the <u>upper</u> note.

1 With small intervals, try to remember how many tones / semitones the interval contains. For instance, the intervals measured downwards from C are

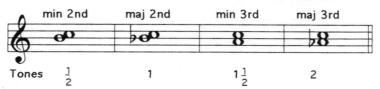

2 For perfect 4ths and 5ths, remember the rule which you already know. This works <u>downwards</u> as well as <u>upwards</u>.

■ | Except when using F and B together **White** goes to **White**   **Black** goes to **Black** |

3 To draw, for example, a major 6th below C. Six letter names down from C is E, but though E is a 6th below, it is a minor not a major 6th. To get the required major 6th, the C cannot be altered because it is the given note, so the interval can only be widened by lowering E to E♭ thus giving a major 6th.

Exercise 14 Draw the following intervals <u>below</u> the given notes.

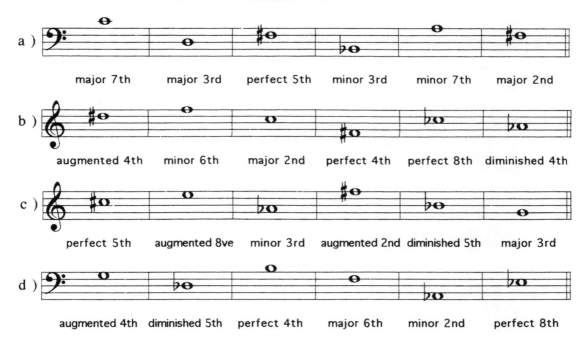

Exercise 15 Name these bracketed intervals. Remember to look at the key signature.

Mozart: Pf. sonata no.13

These tunes provide some revision in major and minor keys.

Exercise 16 Sing these tunes using solfa names. Make hand signs or tap the beats as you sing.

Exercise 17 Having sung the given opening, add another 4 bars to make an 8-bar melody ending on the tonic. Complete the phrasing and add some expression.

■ When the given phrase begins with an up-beat, remember to begin the answering phrase also with an up-beat (at the end of bar 4). This gives a good rhythmic balance between the phrases.

9   SINGING with SOLFA 2 : LEAPS to *m* (major)

●   This group of tunes introduces leaps to *m* in the major key. These are *l - m* and *t - m*.

Exercise 18 These are practice drills to learn the new leaps to *m*. Change the pitch of the starting note where necessary so that the range is comfortable.

Exercise 19 Sing the following melodies with solfa names.

Exercise 20 Compose an answering 4 bars to complete the given opening. Sing the completed melody and add a tempo mark and some expression.

THE C CLEF : TENOR STAVE

The Alto stave, which has been studied already, has <u>middle C</u> as its <u>3rd</u> stave line.

The Alto clef, known also as the C clef, is so drawn that its curves are above and below the 3rd stave line, that is Middle C.

The Tenor stave has middle C as its <u>4th</u> stave line. It is drawn by positioning the C Clef on the 4th stave line.

These are the names of the lines and spaces on the alto and tenor staves. Middle C is drawn as a broken line to make clear that the lines above are 'borrowed' from the treble stave, and the lines below are 'borrowed' from the bass stave.

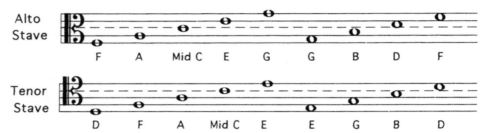

Music for the viola is written on the alto stave, while the tenor stave is used for the tenor trombone and for the high notes of the 'cello and the bassoon.

Exercise 21 Give the letter names for the following notes.

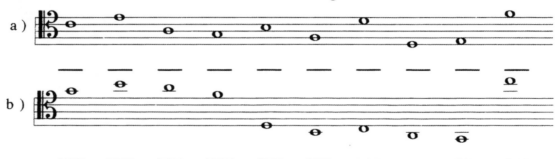

Exercise 22 Transcribe these notes at the same pitch onto the tenor stave. Middle C is drawn on each stave as a guide.

● The pattern of sharps in a key signature is the same for treble, bass and alto but notice how the shape changes at * on the tenor stave.

The pattern of flats in a key signature is the same for all clefs.

■ A key signature is <u>never</u> written on ledger <u>lines</u>.

11 TRIAD INVERSION

■ Every triad, whether major or minor, consists of 3 notes: a root, a 3rd and a 5th.
<u>These names stay attached to the notes to identify them.</u>

● A triad can appear in three positions.

Root position Here the root is the lowest note sounded.

First inversion The root moves up an 8ve. The lowest note sounded is the 3rd of the triad.

Second inversion The root and the 3rd have moved up an 8ve. The lowest note sounded is the 5th of the triad.

Exercise 23 Draw these <u>major</u> tonic triads in the specified positions. Use key signatures.

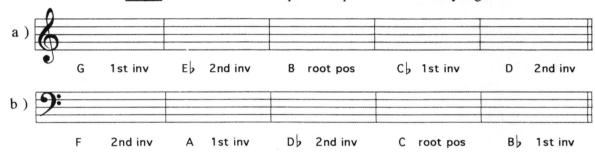

a) G 1st inv   E♭ 2nd inv   B root pos   C♭ 1st inv   D 2nd inv

b) F 2nd inv   A 1st inv   D♭ 2nd inv   C root pos   B♭ 1st inv

Exercise 24 Draw these <u>minor</u> tonic triads in the specified positions. Use key signatures.

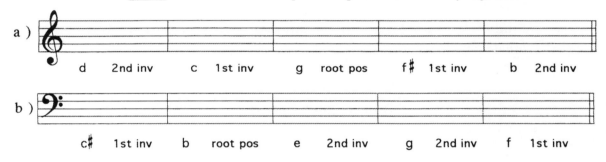

a) d 2nd inv   c 1st inv   g root pos   f♯ 1st inv   b 2nd inv

b) c♯ 1st inv   b root pos   e 2nd inv   g 2nd inv   f 1st inv

Exercise 25 These are major or minor triads in 1st or 2nd inversion. (i) Name the position and type of each triad. (ii) Rewrite each triad in root position. Follow the example.

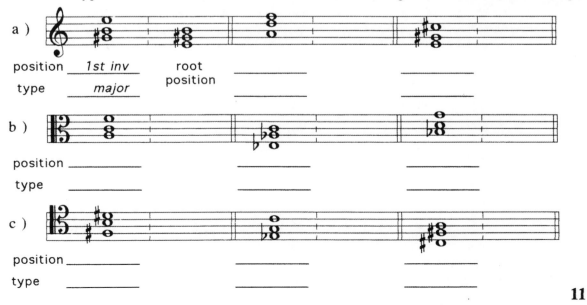

a)
position _1st inv_   root position _____   _____
type _major_   _____   _____

b)
position _____   _____   _____
type _____   _____   _____

c)
position _____   _____   _____
type _____   _____   _____

11

WORD RHYTHM : 4 LINE STANZAS

Study of word rhythm prepares for setting words to music. From early times people have felt a need to express themselves in rhythmical speech, i.e. in poetry. This led naturally to setting words to music in songs. Think of the range of songs from lullabies to war songs and you realise how instinctive this is to our nature.

The first steps in learning to set words to music are basic and rather technical. Do not be discouraged. Later, you will progress to acquiring a very rewarding skill.

● To revise the writing of word rhythms, see 'Music Workout' Grade 5, pp 6, 22, 62. The following are some additional points.

Syllables

1 Words of 2 or more syllables are usually split by hyphens. But note the following:

 (i) A syllable should begin with a consonant, except for suffixes like *-ing, -er.*

 (ii) Double consonants should normally be split: *wan - der, mat - ter.* But always think how words are said; *fall - ing* (not *fal - ling*); *be-tween* (not *bet - ween*). Be sensitive to the sound of words and use judgment when deciding.

2 Every syllable needs a note. To make reading clear, position the note directly above the syllable.

Small words / syllables   Small words like *'the' ' and' 'in' 'a'* should never come at the beginning of a bar. This also applies to prefixes like *'be-' 'in-' 'ex-' 'un-'* etc.

Stresses   In a 4-line stanza, as a rule aim to find <u>two</u> or <u>four</u> main stresses in each line. These words will come on the first beat of a bar, giving 2 or 4 bars per line. Study this example, noting the stresses and hyphens. Each line corresponds to a musical phrase.

> Flý a - way, flý a - way, ó - ver the séa,
> Sún - loving swál - low, for súm - mer is dóne.
> Cóme a - gain, cóme a - gain, cóme back to mé,
> Bring - ing the súm - mer and bring - ing the sún.   (C. Rossetti)

'*Fly a - way*' is 3 more or less equal syllables, so a time of $\frac{3}{4}$ seems likely.

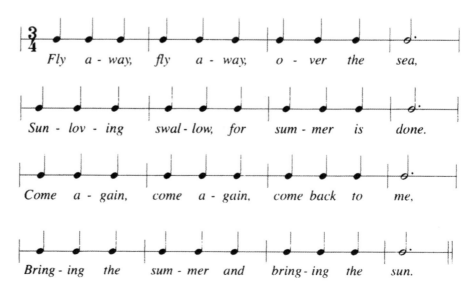

■ Notice that the time signature is written only once.

● The foregoing is accurate, but rhythmically boring. To vary the rhythm try

changing  , but only where the syllable

under the quaver is unimportant. For example:

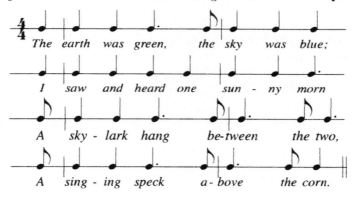

Anacrusis In English, most lines of poetry begin with up-beats. Normally, if the first line has an up-beat to start, so will the other lines. Consider this example:

> The éarth was green, the ský was blue :
> I sáw and heard one sún - ny morn
> A ský - lark hang be - twéen the two.
> A síng - ing speck a - bóve the corn.   C. Rossetti

Two accents per line = 2 bars. 'earth was green, the' is 4 syllables, so $\frac{4}{4}$ is likely.

Notice that only the last line of notes ends with a bar line. This is because the up-beats to lines 2, 3 and 4 really belong to the preceding bars.

Exercise 26 Write rhythms to match the following stanzas:

a) "I toss the branches up and down
      And shake them to and fro.
   I whirl the leaves in flocks of brown.
      And send them high and low."   Anon.

.... Words

WORD RHYTHM : 4 line STANZA EXERCISES

b) *"You are old, Father William," the young man said,*
And your hair has become very white;
And yet you incessantly stand on your head.
Do you think, at your age, it is right?"   Lewis Carroll

_____

.... Words

_____

....

_____

....

_____

....

c) *"At first he came to the farmer's fence*
Where the hedge was thick and the shadows dense;
He saw the barns, and he hied him hence,
All on a summer's night, O!"   Anon

_____

.... Words

_____

....

_____

....

_____

....

d) *"When the green woods laugh with the voice of joy,*
And the dimpling stream runs laughing by;
When the air does laugh with our merry wit,
And the green hill laughs with the noise of it."   William Blake

_____

.... Words

_____

....

_____

....

_____

15

Study this extract from a nocturne by Field. Then answer the questions below.

1.(a) The extract begins and ends in E minor. Name its relative major. _____

  (b) Some notes from bar 1 are listed below. Give the technical name for each (tonic, supertonic etc.)

    B :_____   C :_____   E :_____   G :_____

  (c) Fully describe the bracketed intervals in line 3 of the extract.

    a _____   b_____   c _____

  (d) Circle 3 groups of 3 adjacent notes forming the triads below. Mark each **x, y** or **z**.
    x tonic triad in root pos.   **y** tonic triad in 2nd inv.   **z** tonic triad of the relative major.

2.(a) Add the missing rests at * in bars 6 and 7.

  (b) Add the missing barlines in line 3 of the extract.

  (c) Explain double-dotted notes. _____

  (d) Explain (i)___5___ in the extract. _____

        _____

        (ii)___7___ in the extract._____

        _____

3.(a) Which bar contains part of a chromatic scale?____

  (b) Give the letter name of the highest note in the extract. ____

  (c) Draw <u>one</u> note equal in value to the first 12 notes in bar 5.____

  (d) Explain (i) **Lento** _____

        (ii) ♪ = 100 _____

  (e) Transcribe these notes onto the alto stave at the same pitch.

TEST 1

Q. 1 Name the major key belonging to each key signature. Then write the tonic triad of each key in 1st inversion.

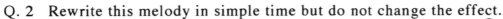

Key ___   Key ___   Key ___

Q. 2 Rewrite this melody in simple time but do not change the effect.

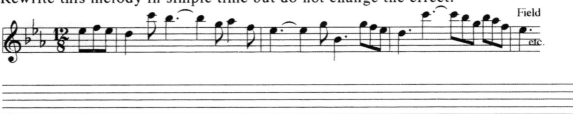

Q. 3 Draw these intervals <u>below</u> the given notes.

perfect 5th   minor 3rd   major 6th   major 7th   diminished 5th   augmented 2nd

Q. 4 Transcribe these notes onto the tenor stave at the same pitch.

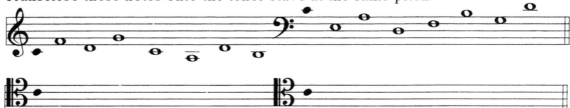

Q.5 Compose an answering 4 bars to complete this melody. Add marks of phrasing, tempo and expression.

Q.6 Write a rhythm for this stanza.

" While I am lying on the grass
   Thy twofold shout I hear;
   From hill to hill it seems to pass,
   At once far off and near. "

W. Wordsworth

.... Words

PART 2
TRANSCRIBING to the TENOR STAVE

● When transcribing music from the treble or bass to the tenor stave, the following points should be remembered.

1 The <u>pitch</u> of the notes is <u>not changed</u>, only their appearance on the stave.

2 Use middle C as a 'yardstick'.

3 The melodic shape is unchanged. Notes on lines stay on lines; notes in spaces stay in spaces.

4 Sharp key signatures have a different pattern on the tenor stave.

Exercise 27 Rewrite these scales at the same pitch on the tenor stave. Include the key signature.

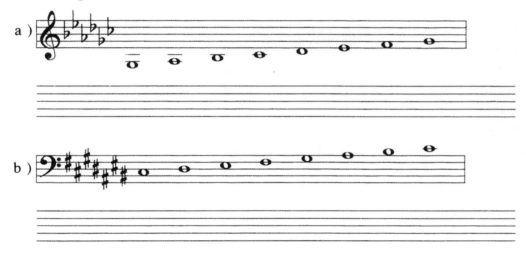

Exercise 28 Transcribe each of these melodies onto the tenor stave. Include the key signature.

| TWO NEW MINOR KEYS : G♯ and B♭ |

■ Revise the points about minor scales and their key signatures on page 75.

● This is the scale of B major, followed by its relative minor G♯ in harmonic and melodic forms.

In both forms of the G♯ minor scale notice that, because the 7th note (leading note) is already sharpened, it becomes F double sharp when raised a semitone. It cannot be called G although this is its <u>sound</u>. The reason is that there is already a note with the letter G, i.e. G♯. Using a key signature, G♯ minor scale is written thus :

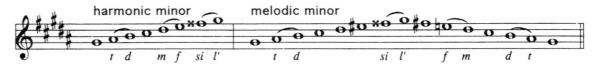

● This is the scale of D♭ major, followed by its relative minor B♭ in harmonic and melodic forms.

Using a key signature, B♭ minor scale is written thus:

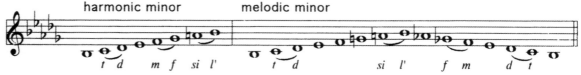

Notice that the 6th and 7th notes when raised become <u>naturals</u>.

Exercise 29   Using key signatures and the <u>bass</u> clef, write the scales of G♯ and B♭ in melodic minor form, ascending and descending.

a)

b)

A PAGE of MINOR SCALES

Exercise 30 Add the clef and the key signature as directed to make these minor scales. Use the form indicated. Mark the semitones. Draw the tonic triad with accidentals.

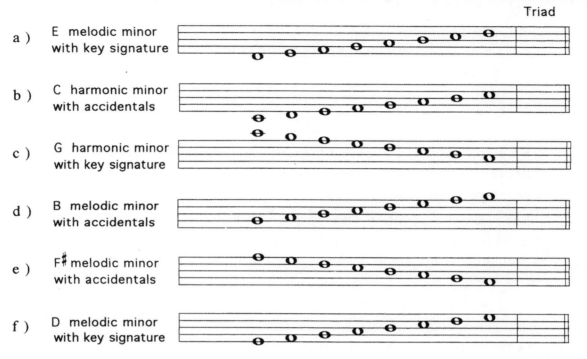

Triad

a) E melodic minor with key signature

b) C harmonic minor with accidentals

c) G harmonic minor with key signature

d) B melodic minor with accidentals

e) F# melodic minor with accidentals

f) D melodic minor with key signature

Exercise 31 Write one octave ascending and descending of each of the minor scales for which the key signature is given. State which scale form you are using.

a) Form _____

b) Form _____

c) Form _____

d) Form _____

e) Form _____

f) Form _____

g) Form _____

Twentieth century composers frequently use 'uneven' metres of 5 and 7 beats per bar to achieve a sense of rhythmic excitement or restlessness in their music.

A time signature with 5 beats per bar is known as **quintuple** time. Two common examples are ⅝ and ⅝. A time signature with five beats is really a combination of two regular bars of 3 + 2 or 2 + 3.

Study this example to notice that, although the main stress falls on the first beat in each bar, some bars show a clear division of 3 + 2 (bars two and four) while bar three shows a division of 2 + 3.

Examples of **septuple** time are ⅞ and ⅞. A bar with seven beats is made with various combinations of 2, 3 or 4 beats. Study the following example to see the different divisions within some bars.

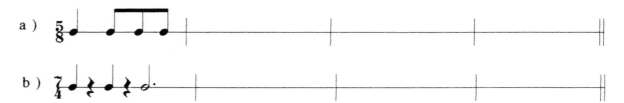

In these irregular times the strong and weak beats within a bar do not form a regular pattern as is the case in normal simple and compound times.

Exercise 32 Finish each rhythm by filling in the blank bars. Clap it when completed.

Exercise 33 Add the missing bar lines in the following extracts. Then clap each rhythm, first slowly, then at a faster speed. Feel how the irregular accentuation creates a real sense of energy in the rhythm.

MORE EXERCISES : IRREGULAR TIME

Exercise 34   Add the missing bar lines in these extracts. Then clap each rhythm.

Exercise 35   Fill in the time signature in each of the following extracts. Add the missing rest at each place marked *

INVERSION of INTERVALS

You have learnt that triads can be inverted. Intervals may also be inverted. This can be done in one of two ways:

1 By bringing the <u>lower</u> note <u>up</u> an octave.
2 By bringing the <u>upper</u> note <u>down</u> an octave.

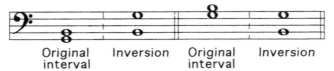

Original interval   Inversion   Original interval   Inversion

As in triad inversion, it is important that each note retains its identity, i.e. its letter name. In the original interval above, the two notes used are G and B. In the inversion the two notes are also G and B.

Although the note names do not alter in the inversion, <u>two</u> changes do happen.

1 The size (numerical value) of the interval changes. Measuring the inversion in the example, the 3rd becomes a 6th.

All inverted intervals change their size. To check this, work out the numerical value of the inversions of the following intervals which start on G.

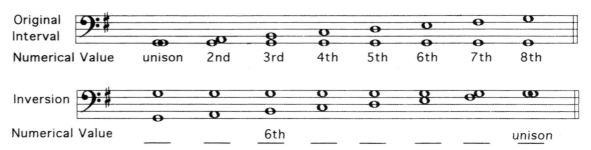

	unison	2nd	3rd	4th	5th	6th	7th	8th

Numerical Value   unison   2nd   3rd   4th   5th   6th   7th   8th

Numerical Value   ___   ___   6th   ___   ___   ___   ___   unison

Now try adding together the numerical value of any interval and its inversion. In the example above, take 3 + 6 = 9. Check whether other pairs add up to 9.

> To find the numerical value of an inversion, subtract the numerical value of the original interval from 9.

2 The other change that happens when an interval is inverted is a change in the quality name. For example, G - B is a major 3rd but the inversion is a minor 6th.

3rd   6th

Here are some more examples of intervals and their inversions,

maj 3rd   min 6th   min 3rd   maj 6th   aug 2nd   dim 7th   dim 5th   aug 4th   perf 4th   perf 5th

Do you notice the pattern of quality change in the inversions? It can be summed up in the following formula. Learn it by heart.

> **When an interval is inverted**
> Major becomes Minor   Minor becomes Major
> Augmented becomes Diminished   Diminished becomes Augmented
> Perfect remains Perfect

Exercise 36 (i) Describe each interval.
            (ii) Beside each one draw its inversion.
           (iii) Describe the inversion.

      The first one has been done as a guide.

a)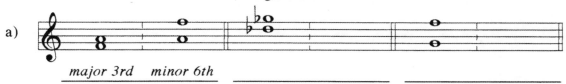

         major 3rd   minor 6th

b)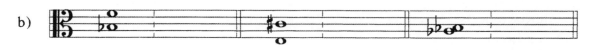

c)

d)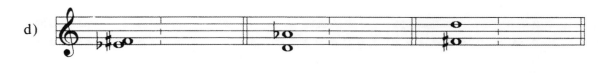

e)

f)

■ Interval inversion can be useful when calculating a large interval <u>below</u> a given note, e.g. a minor 7th below D. The inversion of a minor 7th is a major 2nd, i.e. D to E. 'Re-invert' the interval by bringing E down an 8ve, thereby producing a minor 7th. Double check the numerical value and quality by measuring <u>upwards</u> from E in the usual way.

Exercise 37 Draw the following intervals <u>below</u> the given notes.

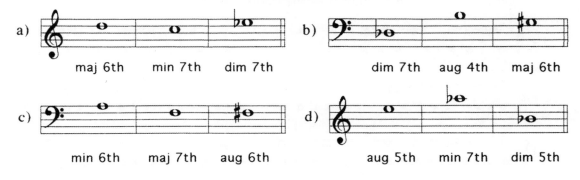

a)   maj 6th   min 7th   dim 7th   b)   dim 7th   aug 4th   maj 6th

c)   min 6th   maj 7th   aug 6th   d)   aug 5th   min 7th   dim 5th

● This group of exercises introduces the semiquaver rest and the tied semiquaver. The effect of the two is similar but in the latter the sound is unbroken.

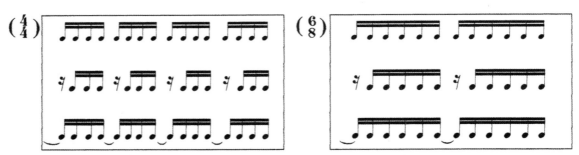

Exercise 38 Practise clapping these patterns. The first pattern in each table is one you know. Use it to help with the new patterns by clapping them alternately.

Exercise 39 Watch for the new rhythms as you clap these exercises. Keep a steady beat.

● The next group of exercises introduces two further semiquaver combinations in compound time. These are marked * .

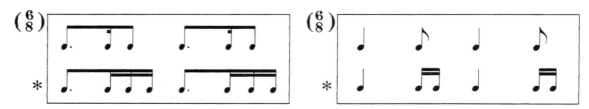

Exercise 40 Alternate the clapping of these paired rhythms a few times. When the new patterns are secure, clap the following exercises.

●   If a triad has all its notes as close to each other as possible, the triad is said to be
in **'close position'**. If the notes are spaced out, i.e. where other triad notes can be
fitted in between, they are in **'open position'**.

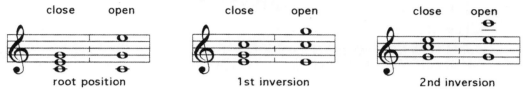

An 'open position' triad is still described as being in root position, 1st inversion
or 2nd inversion, depending on which of its notes is at the bottom. Its upper notes
can appear in any order.

Exercise 41   Rewrite each <u>major</u> tonic triad in open position. Underneath, state the key and
the triad position (root position, 1st or 2nd inversion). Follow example in bar 1.

Key   *F*   *1st inv*

Exercise 42   Now do the same with these <u>minor</u> tonic triads

Key

Exercise 43   Rewrite each triad in close position. Name the key (major or minor) and state
the triad position (root position, 1st or 2nd inversion). Follow the example.

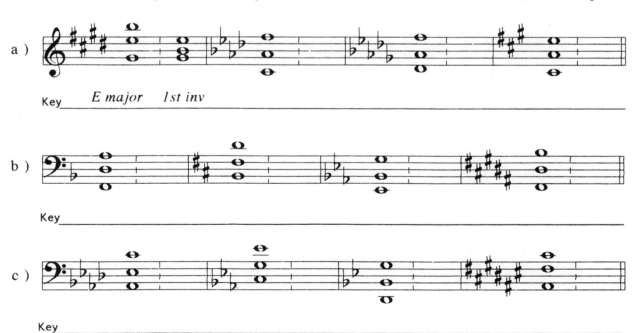

a)

Key   *E major*   *1st inv*

b)

Key

c)

Key

● When transposing melodies in major keys, keep these points in mind.

1 A melody in a <u>major</u> key always transposes to another <u>major</u> key.

2 The 'interval of transposition' is the interval between the tonic of the original key and the tonic of the new key.

3 The key signature of the new key must be included in the transposed melody.

4 The shape of the transposed melody must match the shape of the original one. Use solfa names to help you. Remember that tunes don't always begin on *do*!

Exercise 44 Revise measuring intervals (pages 6 - 7) before doing this exercise.

i) Name the major key for each signature and write its tonic. (ii) Transpose each note putting in the new signature. The first on each line is done as a guide.

Exercise 45 Transpose the tune up or down the required intervals. Give the new key signature.

" The Lass of Richmond Hill "

● **Major keys** New leaps to *d* are introduced. These are *l - d* and *f - d*. Practise these drills to learn the new intervals. Adjust starting pitch to suit.

Exercise 46 These melodies contain the new leaps to *d*. Sing using solfa names.

● **Minor keys** You know *l - d*, as both are notes of the minor tonic triad. *f - d* which you learnt above is the same distance in both major and minor keys. So look out for it in these minor key melodies.

COMPLETING 8-Bar MELODIES

The next stage in composing a melody involves the completion of an 8-bar tune of which only the first 2 bars are given.

Phrasing Simple 8-bar melodies break naturally into two halves which form a type of ' question and answer '. The first half ends in bar 4, usually <u>not</u> on the tonic, while the second half answers, finishing on the tonic in bar 8. A long note value in bar 4 will help to mark the end of the first half.

Some 4-bar phrases may need to be subdivided into shorter sections, especially where there are a lot of notes. This is like the need for a comma in a long sentence. Sing or play these examples and study the points made about phrasing.

'Golden Slumbers'

This 8-bar extract breaks naturally into two phrases, each containing 4 bars. It needs no further division.

'Happy Birthday'

'Happy Birthday' is an 8-bar melody. It has two main 4-bar phrases, each of which breaks again into shorter 2 bar units. So the phrasing pattern is 2 + 2 + 2 + 2.

When continuing a melody, it may be a help if you break up the task. Do this by first sketching a good rhythmic framework, and then working on the pitch.

It is most important to sing the melody, so at this stage aim to write a melody which you can sing confidently. Go over it frequently from the beginning as new bars are added and the melody grows. This helps to achieve the following.

   a) A natural and interesting <u>shape</u>. Simple shapes can be surprisingly effective.
   b) Continuation of the <u>character</u> and <u>style</u> of the given opening.
   c) Maintenance of the correct <u>balance</u>.

■ Always look carefully at any music you sing or play, or are required to work on, paying attention to the rhythm, the phrasing and the melodic shape.

As a sample exercise, complete the melody below to make a total of 8 bars. When you have finished, phrase the tune, choose a tempo mark and add some expression.

■ Break up your working into the following stages:

   i) Sing the given opening.
   ii) Complete the first half by writing another 2 bars.
   iii) Write an answering 4 bars to finish the melody.

8 - BAR MELODY EXERCISES

Exercise 47 Complete these melodies to make a total of 8 bars in each. Add phrasing, tempo and expression marks.

THE BAROQUE PERIOD

This is a brief introduction to an important period in musical history. Its purpose is to start you off investigating the subject on your own. Consult your school or local library. Use encyclopaedias to obtain information and find definitions of specialist words and ideas as you come across these. Listen to music and composers of the period to get to know them. Classical music programmes broadcast a great variety of Baroque music, and many reasonably-priced recordings are now available. Even better, try to go to concerts to experience the impact of live performance.

The Baroque period includes the 17th and the first half of the 18th centuries. Used to describe works of art and architecture, the name was later applied to music. It may come from *barocco*, a Portuguese word to describe an oddly-shaped pearl. The term was used by critics to suggest that the music was unrefined or too ornate, but this was a time of great musical innovation. These are some of the important developments.

Keys The system of modes invented by the ancient Greeks was being discontinued except in plainsong and folk music. The '*do*' mode (Ionian) and the '*la*' mode (Aeolian) gradually became the basis of the major and minor scales as we know them today. So the foundation of the major / minor scheme of musical keys was laid at this time.

Stringed instruments The '*viol*' group of 6-stringed instruments, with frets like the guitar but played with a bow, was replaced by the 4-stringed unfretted violin family. The orchestra evolved. At first this consisted of a group of string players, with brass, woodwind and percussion players added occasionally.

Keyboard instruments The **harpsichord** was used in orchestras to emphasise the string bass line and fill out the harmonies. The harpsichordist played throughout the piece and came to be called the 'continuo' player. The **clavichord** was used in the home. In church, the **organ** was popular. Much Baroque keyboard music is written for these instruments because the piano was invented only in the early 18th century.

Instrumental and **Vocal Music** Longer works for instruments were written, e.g.
> suite   sonata   concerto   concerto grosso   fugue

For voice new kinds of works were
> opera   cantata   oratorio

General style It was fashionable to include many new features in compositions, e.g.
> **counterpoint** involving fugue and imitative writing
> **melodic decoration** with many ornamental features (See page 59.)
> **use of contrast** in dynamics, instrumental sound (timbre) and ensemble size

Exercise 48 These exercises should involve <u>research</u> using resources.

(a) Devise a table of the different kinds of works mentioned under 'Instrumental and Vocal Music' above. For each kind give a clear definition and a short informative note.

(b) Find out about these composers. Make a chart like that suggested below. Fill in the information you obtain. Decorate it with pictures of the composers.

Monteverdi   Vivaldi   Scarlatti   Corelli   J.S.Bach   Handel   Purcell   Couperin

Composer	Birth Year	Death Year	Nationality	Names of three well-known compositions

(c) Choose <u>one</u> of the composers named above. Investigate his life in greater detail to enable you to write a short article suitable for a school newspaper or magazine.

GENERAL OBSERVATION 2

Study this extract from Tchaikovsky's 6th Symphony. Then answer the questions.

1. (a) Name the key of the opening. _____

   (b) Name the relative of this key. _____

   (c) Add the missing time signature in bar 1.

   (d) Explain ♪♪♪ _____

2. (a) Give technical names for the first two notes in bar 1 _____ and _____

   and the first two notes in bar 4 _____ and _____

   (b) Fully describe the bracketed intervals in the following bars:

   bar 2 _____ bar 6 _____

   bars 8-9_____ bar19 _____

   (c) Comparing bars 1 - 2 with bars 3 - 4, what do you observe?_____

   _____

   Comparing bars 1 - 4 with bars 9 -12, what do you observe?

   _____

3. (a) Explain (i) **Allegro con grazia** _____ (ii) *più f* _____

   (b) How many times does the rhythmic pattern ♩ ♩ ♫♫ ♩ ♩ appear?_____

   (c) How many times does the rhythmic pattern ♪. ♪♪. ♪ ♩. appear?_____

   (d) The opening melody is played by cellos. Rewrite bars 1 - 4 on the tenor stave at the same pitch - this is how it would be written for cellists.

32

Q.1   Write one octave ascending and descending of the scale of G♯ melodic minor.
Use a key signature, add necessary accidentals and mark the semitones.

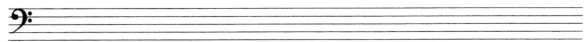

Q.2   Transcribe this melody to the alto stave at the same pitch.

Schumann: Piano Concerto

Q.3(a)   Add the remaining barlines to this melody.

  (b)   Add the time signature. Where * is marked, complete the bar with a rest.

Q.4   (i) Describe each interval.   (ii) Draw and name the inversion of each.

Q.5   Rewrite each tonic triad in close position. Name the key (major / minor) and the
triad position (root pos, 1st inv, 2nd inv.)

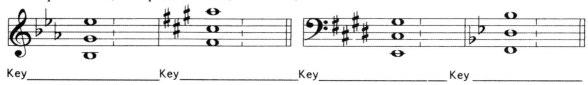

Key_____   Key_____   Key_____   Key _____

Q.6   Transpose this tune down a major 3rd. Give the new key signature.

Q.7   Finish this melody to make 8 bars in all. Add phrasing, tempo and expression marks.

● When transposing a melody up or down an octave, these points will be helpful.

   1 Draw middle C on each stave as a point of reference.

   2 Double check the position of the first note.

   3 Keep the shape of the melody the same.

   4 Notes on lines change to being in spaces. Notes in spaces change to being on lines.

   5 The pattern of sharp key signatures is different on the tenor stave.

Exercise 49 Transpose each melody down an octave and write it on the given stave.

Exercise 50 Transpose each melody up an octave, writing it on the given stave.

Any triad consists of a root, 3rd and 5th. As well as building a triad on the tonic, triads may be built on the supertonic, the mediant etc. Study this diagram.

Triad name   tonic   supertonic   mediant   subdominant   dominant   submediant   leading note

The triads built on the tonic, the subdominant and the dominant are used most often to harmonise tunes, so these are studied first. They are easy to recognise as the 'chords' guitarists use to accompany songs. They are known as the **primary triads**. In major keys primary triads are all major triads.

Here are the primary triads with their solfa names. Sing each triad to solfa names; then play the triad notes together.

Writing 'tonic', 'subdominant' and 'dominant' to name triads can be cumbersome, so a kind of short-hand is used. Roman numerals are written instead of names to identify the root of each triad. Study this example to see how the numerals are used.

tonic   subdominant   dominant

■ Use large numerals for **major** triads **I IV V**.

Practise singing this exercise to learn the notes which make up each primary triad.

Exercise 51   Draw the primary triads in these major keys, using key signatures. Follow the example in bar 1. Write a roman numeral under each triad.

a)

Key G :   I   IV   V   F :   B♭ :

b)

A♭ :   D :   E :

Exercise 52   i) Name the major key indicated by each key signature.

ii) Identify the primary triad in each key by writing a roman numeral below.

a)

Key _B_   tr **IV**   K___ tr___   K___ tr___   K___ tr___   K___ tr___   K___ tr___

b)

Key ___ tr___   K ___ tr___   K ___ tr___   K ___ tr___   K ___ tr___   K ___ tr___

PRIMARY TRIADS : MINOR KEYS

● Triads can be built on any note of a minor scale, just as they can on any note of a major scale. The harmonic minor is usually the form of scale used.

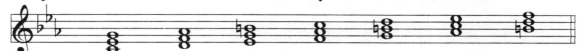

Triad name   tonic   supertonic   mediant   subdominant   dominant   submediant   leading note

As with major keys, the most used triads are the tonic, subdominant and dominant. In minor keys as well as major ones, these are called the primary triads.

Here they are with their solfa names. Sing each triad to solfa names. Then play the triad notes together.

l   d   m   r   f   l'   m   si   t'

■ Notice that in <u>minor</u> keys **i** and **iv** are <u>minor triads</u>, whereas **V** is a <u>major triad</u>.

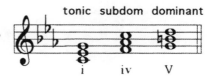

■ | Small numerals are used for **minor** triads, <u>large</u> for major triads. |

Practise singing this exercise to learn the notes which form each primary triad in the minor key.

l   d   m   r   f   l'   m   si   t'   l'

■ The 3rd of V is the raised leading note (*si*). It will <u>always</u> have an accidental.

Exercise 53   Draw the primary triads in these minor keys, using key signatures. Follow the example in bar 1. Write a roman numeral under each triad.

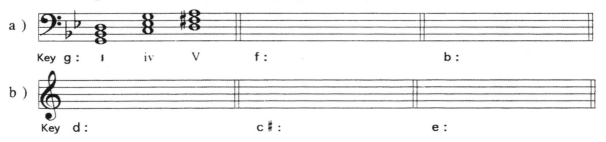

Exercise 54   i) Name the minor key indicated by each key signature.
          ii) Identify the primary triad in each key by writing a roman numeral below.

Use the following group of clapping exercises to improve your fluency in reading in these times : $\frac{2}{2}$, $\frac{3}{2}$, $\frac{3}{8}$ and in $\frac{6}{4}$, $\frac{9}{4}$, $\frac{6}{16}$.

Exercise 55 Count in full beats while clapping.

TRANSPOSITION with CHROMATIC NOTES

Melodies, especially those in major keys, may include 'chromatic' notes, that is, notes which do not belong to the key of the melody. When transposing melodies with chromatic notes, care is needed. The following guidelines are helpful.

1 Chromatic notes have usually been raised or lowered a semitone.

2 Any note which has an accidental in the original melody <u>must</u> have one in the transposed version, provided key signatures are used for both versions.

3 A note which has <u>no</u> accidental in the original melody <u>should not</u> have one in the transposed version, provided key signatures are used for both versions.

4 Accidentals in the transposed melody may or may not be the same as those in the original melody.

5 In relation to each chromatic note always ask these questions :
   a) In the original melody does the accidental raise or lower the note? Or does it restore it to what it should be in the key?
   b) How is a similar raising, lowering or restoring achieved in the new key?

Study this example of a melody transposed into 4 different keys. Give particular attention to the accidentals in the transposed versions.

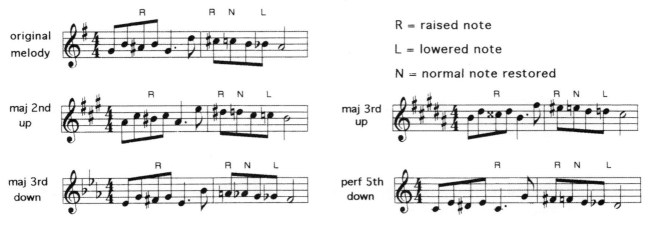

R = raised note

L = lowered note

N = normal note restored

Exercise 56 Transpose the following melodies up a major 3rd.

a) Brahms: Sym. no. 3

b) Mozart: Sym. no. 40

When transposing melodies, the character of the melody should not change. Therefore major melodies transpose to major keys; minor ones to minor keys.

Transposing up

This melody in E <u>minor</u> is to be transposed into the minor key a perfect 5th above.

l si, l t   d r m r   m f m si l'   l

1 A perfect 5th above E is B, so the new key is B <u>minor.</u>
2 The next step is to draw the key signature of B minor.
3 It may help to write out the scales of E minor and B minor with solfa names.

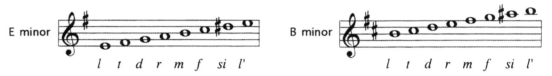

E minor   *l t d r m f si l'*   B minor   *l t d r m f si l'*

4 Once the key signature and the position of the first note are worked out, it is easy to follow the shape of the melody by using the solfa names in the new key. Remember that melodies do not <u>always</u> begin on the tonic.

l si, l t   d r m r   m f m si l'   l

Transposing down

In this example the original melody in E minor is to be transposed down a major 3rd.

1 A major 3rd down from E is C, so the new key is C <u>minor.</u>
2 These are the scales of E minor and C minor.

E minor   *l t d r m f si l'*   C minor   *l t d r m f si l'*

3 Once the key signature and the position of the first note are drawn, the shape of the melody is easily followed by using the solfa names in the new key.

l si, l t   d r m r   m f m si l'   l

■ **Points to remember when transposing**

The **interval of transposition** is the interval between the tonic of the original key and the tonic of the new key.

Do not confuse major / minor **intervals of transposition** with major / minor **keys**.

Major keys transpose to **major keys**. **Minor keys** transpose to **minor keys**.

MINOR KEY TRANSPOSITION EXERCISES

■ When working through these exercises, remember that in a minor key, a raised 6th (*fi*) may appear as well as a raised 7th (*si*).

Exercise 57 Transpose these minor melodies into minor keys a <u>major 2nd (a tone) lower</u>.

"Charlie is my Darling" (Scotland)

a)

"The Miller of the Dee" (England)

b)

Exercise 58 Transpose these minor melodies into minor keys a <u>minor 3rd higher</u>.

Bach: Orchestral Suite No. 2

a)

Grieg: Anitra's Dance ("Peer Gynt")

b)

Exercise 59 Transpose these minor melodies into minor keys a <u>perfect 4th lower</u>.

Brahms: "St. Antony" Variations

a)

Beethoven: "Egmont Overture"

b)

SINGING with SOLFA 4 : SOME LEAPS to *l* (minor)

● These melodies introduce two new leaps to *l* in the minor key. They are: *r - l* and *f - l*

Exercise 60 Use these drills to practise learning the new leaps to *l*.

Exercise 61 Sing these melodies with solfa names. Tap a steady beat or make hand signs.

Exercise 62 Sing the opening. Add 2 bars to finish the first half of the tune. Write 4 more bars to complete the tune - 8 bars in all. Add phrasing, tempo and expression marks.

Word rhythms in ³/₄ time have already been studied. Look at the stanza on p.12 where the rhythm produced a time of ³/₄ with four bars per line. Here it is again but this time only two accents are marked. Notice how the rhythm becomes less heavy-footed.

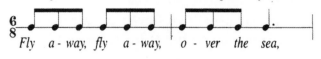

"Fly a - way, fly a - way, o - ver the sea,"

"*Fly a - way, fly a - way*" has 6 more or less equal syllables, so a time of ⁶/₈ suits.

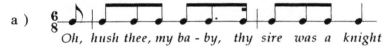

Fly a - way, fly a - way, o - ver the sea,

Patterns Just as in ³/₄ time ♩♩♩ could be varied to ♩. ♪♩ or ♩ ♩. ♪ , so in ⁶/₈ time ♩♩♩ can be varied to ♩. ♪♪ or ♩♪♪ ; these patterns, as well as ♩ ♪ and ♩. are the most usual <u>half-bar</u> patterns in ⁶/₈ time.

Anacrusis An anacrusis (up-beat) in ⁶/₈ time is usually ♪ or ♫ ; don't forget that the very last bar is shortened by the value of the up-beat.

Exercise 63 Complete each of these 4-line stanzas. Each line begins with an anacrusis.

a)

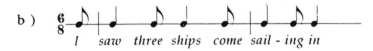

Oh, hush thee, my ba - by, thy sire was a knight

_____

Thy mother a la - dy, both love - ly and bright ;

_____

The woods and the glens, from the tow'rs we see ,

_____

They all are be - long - ing, dear ba - by, to thee .   Walter Scott

b)

I saw three ships come sail - ing in

_____

On Christ - mas Day, on Christ - mas Day ;

_____

I saw three ships come sail - ing in

_____

On Christ - mas Day in the morn - ing .   Anon

c)

Oh, young Loch -in-var is come out of the West ,

_____

Through all the wide Bor - der his steed was the best ,

_____

And save his good broad - sword he wea - pons had none ,

_____

He rode all un - arm'd and he rode all a - lone .   Walter Scott

ARRANGING CHORDS for VOICES

The primary triads are the basis for creating simple harmony in many different styles and mediums. Chord formation is easily heard and seen in much piano, choral, chamber and orchestral music. At this stage we will consider some basic points on arranging chords for a mixed choir made up of soprano, alto, tenor and bass voices. This is known as 'S.A.T.B. choir' for short.

Layout   We begin by using two staves, as in a hymn-tune arrangement. The soprano and alto share the treble stave, while the tenor and bass share the bass stave.

Stems   Because each stave is shared by two voices, the note stems are written in different directions to avoid any confusion. Stems for the upper voice on each stave go upwards, i.e. soprano and tenor. Stems for the lower voice on each stave go downwards, i.e. alto and bass.

Notice that the stems on the bass stave of the first chord are drawn in both directions. This means that the bass <u>and</u> the tenor both sing the same note (unison).

Range   The music for each voice is kept within a comfortable singing range.

  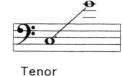 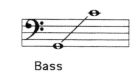

Soprano   Alto   Tenor   Bass

These are the ranges normally used for each voice. But composers sometimes write notes beyond these ranges for special effect. The range expected of a solo singer is generally wider.

Doubling   To produce a 4-part chord, it is necessary to repeat one of the triad notes. The root is normally repeated, i.e. the root is 'doubled'.

Spacing   To create a good balance in the sound of a chord, any gap wider than an octave should normally only occur between tenor and bass parts. (The gap can then be as wide as 1 octave + 5th.) Study the spacing of the voices in this example.

Pitch order   The soprano normally sings the highest note; the alto sings the next lowest; the tenor lower again, while the bass sings the lowest note.

Root position   To begin we will write 4-part chords in root position. This means that the bass voice sings the root note of the chord which will also be doubled in another voice. This is shown in the following example.

 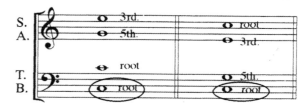

Exercise 64 This hymn-tune phrase uses crotchet values except for the final chord which is a minim. Add stems to each voice. Soprano and alto sing in unison at * .

Exercise 65 Write 3 different root position arrangements of each triad for S. A. T. B. The given note, to be sung by the bass voice, is the root note of the triad.

GENERAL OBSERVATION 3

Study this keyboard extract. Then fill in the blanks to complete each sentence.

Gigue

The piece begins in the key of_____ , but from bars 3 to 7 the key changes

to_____ . The time signature $\frac{12}{8}$ is described as _____ _____

time. The tempo mark 'Presto' means that it will be played at a _____ speed. At

the start the melodic interest is in the_____ hand part, this is then imitated by

the_____ hand. The imitation is ___ octave(s)_____ in pitch. The rhythm

is the same in both hands in bars____ and ____ . Arpeggios are a feature of the piece;

complete arpeggios are played ____ times in this extract. From bar 5 onwards the

texture becomes fuller, with the left hand playing double notes in bars 5 and 6 to

form intervals of_____ and _____ . The boxes at the end of the extract enclose

a sequence. Comparing the two, we notice that the rhythm is _____ . The

pitch of the second is a_____ _____ than the first.

This gigue, the final dance of a Suite, was composed by Handel who lived in the

_____ period. The keyboard instrument for which it was originally written

was the_____ .

TEST 3

Q.1   Write the key signature of each of these keys followed by its tonic triad in root position, 1st inversion and 2nd inversion.

B flat minor   F♯ major

Q.2(a) Name the key of this melody. _____   (b) Describe each of the marked intervals.

1 _____ 2 _____ 3 _____ 4 _____

Q.3   Name the key belonging to each key signature. Then identify each primary triad by writing its roman numeral beneath.

Key _major_ ____ ____   Key _minor_ ____ ____ ____

Q.4   Transpose this melody which is in A♭ major into the major key a minor 3rd lower.

Q.5   Write 3 different root position arrangements of each triad for S.A.T.B.

Q.6   Finish this melody to make a total of 8 bars. Add phrasing, tempo and expression.

S. A. T. B. : PRIMARY CHORDS in MAJOR KEYS

■ Revise the points on page 42 about arranging a chord for 4-part choir.

● The next stage is to arrange each of the primary triads in major keys for S.A.T.B.

In all major keys   chord I = $\begin{array}{c} s \\ m \\ d \end{array}$ chord IV = $\begin{array}{c} d \\ l \\ f \end{array}$ chord V = $\begin{array}{c} r \\ t \\ s \end{array}$

Organise 3 people to sing each chord so that the harmonic effect can be heard.

Sketch a 'chord plan', like the one below. This helps you to write and recognise chords.

The chord plan identifies a key and shows the notes on the stave which make up each of its primary triads, together with their solfa names and roman numeral.

Key C :   I ⓓ m s   IV ⓕl d   V ⓢt r

Notice the circled root of each chord. This is important for two reasons:

1 It will be the bass note of the chord.
2 It will be repeated (doubled) in another voice.

These are some examples of the primary triads of C major arranged as root position chords for S. A. T. B.

I   I   IV   IV   V   V

■
> **An 'order of work' when writing S. A. T. B. chords.**
>
> 1 Sketch a chord plan.
> 2 Write the root note for the bass voice with its roman numeral below.
> 3 Write the soprano note - choosing any note available in the chord.
> 4 Fill in alto and tenor notes, taking care with spacing.

As a sample exercise, complete the chord plan. Then write root position chords for S. A. T. B. Where the chord is repeated, show different arrangements.

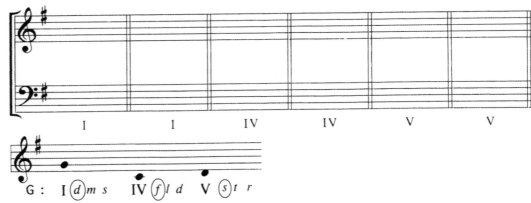

I   I   IV   IV   V   V

G :   I ⓓm s   IV ⓕl d   V ⓢt r

Exercise 66 Complete each chord plan. Then write root position chords for S. A. T. B. as indicated. Where the chord is repeated, show different arrangements.

S. A. T. B. : PRIMARY CHORDS in MINOR KEYS

In all minor keys, chord i = $\begin{array}{c}m\\d\\l\end{array}$ (minor); chord iv = $\begin{array}{c}l\\f\\r\end{array}$ (minor); chord V = $\begin{array}{c}t\\si\\m\end{array}$ (major)
Arrange to sing each triad in parts to hear the harmonic colour.

This is a chord plan in the key of **A minor** :

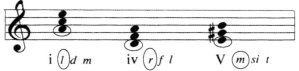

i (l) d m   iv (r) f l   V (m) si t

Although the sound of the chords is different in the minor key, the procedures for writing are the same as before. Remember in all minor keys to include the raised accidental (*si*) in chord V.

Exercise 67 Complete each chord plan. Write root position chords for S. A. T. B. as indicated.

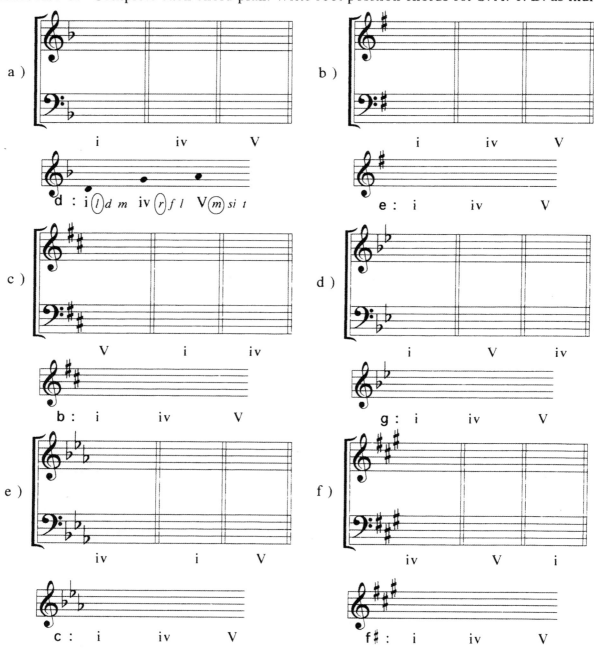

Exercise 68 Sketch a chord plan for each key. Identify each root in the bass by its numeral. Complete each chord by writing notes for S.A.T.

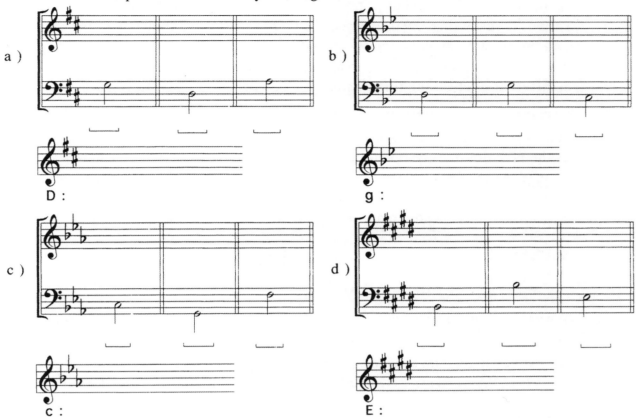

Exercise 69 Name the key and write a chord plan on the stave below each extract. Then identify each chord marked * by writing its numeral.

■ Note : Although the root is <u>normally</u> doubled, this need not always be the case.

■ Having labelled the chords, listen to them in context by playing each extract.

TRANSPOSING INSTRUMENTS

The sound of most instruments is the same as the pitch of their written notes, but there are some instruments whose sound differs from what is written. These are called 'transposing' instruments. The reason for the difference between the sound and the written notes is usually to make playing easier for the performer. The actual sounds produced are said to be at 'concert pitch'. (Instruments can be made in different pitches: the tin whistle may be pitched in C, D, E, E♭, G or B♭.)

Transposition up or down an octave   **piccolo double bass double bassoon**

This is the easiest to understand. An instrument which plays very high notes, such as the piccolo, or very low notes, such as the double bass, would use many ledger lines if the music were written at actual pitch. So the music is written an octave higher or lower than it sounds.

Transposition down a tone - major 2nd   **B♭ horn B♭ trumpet B♭ clarinet**

These instruments are built in B♭. C is the easiest key to read in, so when a performer plays in C, the sound made is a tone lower, B♭.

Transposition down a minor 3rd   **clarinet in A**

Some clarinets are built in A, sounding a minor 3rd lower than written.

Transposition down a perfect 5th   **horn in F   cor anglais**

These instruments sound a perfect 5th lower than written.

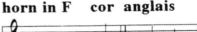

Transposition up a perfect 4th   **trumpet in F**

In the Baroque period a high trumpet was used, sounding a perfect 4th <u>higher</u> than written.

■ When playing together, all instruments must <u>sound</u> in the same key. If the composer wishes all the players to sound the tonic in the key of G, for instance, the music will have to be written as follows for the transposing instruments:

Exercise 70   In each case, double check the necessary pitch change. See page opposite.

a) This is written for a double bass. Write it at concert pitch (sounding pitch).

Schubert: " Unfinished " Symphony

b) This is the <u>sound</u> made by a B♭ clarinet. Write it as it would <u>appear</u> to the player.

Beethoven: Piano Concerto No.3

c) This extract is written for an A clarinet. Rewrite it at concert pitch.

Schubert: " Unfinished "

d) This is the <u>sound</u> made by an A clarinet. Rewrite as it would <u>appear</u> to the player,

Beethoven: Symphony No.7

e) This is written for a horn in F. Rewrite at concert pitch.

Mozart: Horn Concerto No.3

f) This is written for a trumpet in F. Rewrite at concert pitch.

Bach: Brandenburg Concerto No.2

SINGING with SOLFA 5
SOME LEAPS to *t* (major) and to *si* (minor)

●   Leaps to the 7th note of the scale are very common. The two new leaps introduced are the same distance in major and minor keys. They are first shown in major keys.

Exercise 71   Sing these practice drills to learn the new intervals.

Exercise 72   Look out for the new leaps to *t* while singing these melodies.

Exercise 73   The leaps to *t* at the top of the page sound the same when transferred to the minor key. Sing them with solfa names for the minor key as shown.

Exercise 74   Look out for the new leaps to *si* while singing these melodies.

MORE MELODY WRITING

Exercise 75 Using the given opening, compose a melody to make a total of 8 bars. Add suitable marks of tempo, phrasing and expression to the completed melody.

SHORT SCORE : OPEN SCORE

● In 4-part chords (S. A. T. B.) the music is said to be in **short score** when the four parts (voices) are compressed into two staves. When each part (voice) appears on a separate stave, the music is said to be in **open score**.

Study this example. The music is written first in short score, then in open score.

Steiner:" Gott will's machen "

In the <u>open score</u> version, consider each of the following points:

1 **Bar lines** These are drawn through all four staves.

2 **Key signature** This is repeated on <u>each</u> stave.

3 **Time signature** This is repeated on <u>each</u> stave.

4 **Stems** Follow the normal practice, so stems are drawn up or down according to whether noteheads are above or below the middle line of the stave.

5 **Tenor** This part is always written in the <u>treble</u>, an octave higher than the sound. The small **8** under the clef is a reminder of this.

6 **Unisons** In open score, each voice part must show its own note, even if there is a unison, i.e. two voices singing the same note.

Exercise 76 Rewrite the following extract in open score. The notes at the start are given.

Bach: " Liebster Emmanuel "

● To transcribe music from open score to short score, simply reverse the procedures.

1 **Bar lines** These are drawn through both staves.

2 **Key signature** This appears on both staves.

3 **Time signature** This appears on both staves.

4 **Stems** Stems go <u>up</u> for soprano and tenor and <u>down</u> for alto and bass.

5 **Tenor** This voice is written at actual pitch on the bass stave, i.e. an 8ve lower than it appears in open score.

6 **Unison** Where the same note is sung by soprano and alto or by tenor and bass, a note with 2 stems is written. However, when a unison is sung by alto and tenor, the note must appear in both voice parts.

Exercise 77 Rewrite this open score extract in short score.

F. Barthélémon: Morning Hymn

When analysing chords in piano music, be aware of the following points.

The texture of piano music can be quite varied. For example, all the notes of a chord may not be sounded at the same time.

They can be spread in an arpeggio shape.

Or they may be divided between the hands like this.

Notes may be duplicated for a fuller sound.

In a simple texture, a chord may be implied, if only two of its notes are present.

Always play the extracts when you have finished labelling the chords in order to hear them. If you are not a pianist, have someone play them for you. You will be surprised how familiar these sounds are. You hear these chords in some shape or form in the music you play, but you also hear them on radio and TV, in advertisements and even in the supermarket. You are now beginning to label these familar sounds - you can't do that without hearing them!

Exercise 78   Name the key of the extract. Write a chord plan on the short stave. Identify each chord marked * by giving its roman numeral.

Exercise 79 For each extract: (i) name the key; (ii) write a chord plan; (iii) identify each chord marked * by giving its roman numeral.

■ When identifying chords in a passage in open score, remember to check the notes on all the staves, taking account of the different clefs.

Exercise 80 Name the key of each extract. Identify each chord marked * by a roman numeral.

ORNAMENTS

Ornaments, sometimes called 'grace notes', are extra notes played to decorate a melody. They are either written as very small notes in the music, or they are shown by special signs. Music of the Baroque period often used quite a number of ornaments.

These are the principal ornaments, with explanations of how they are to be written and performed.

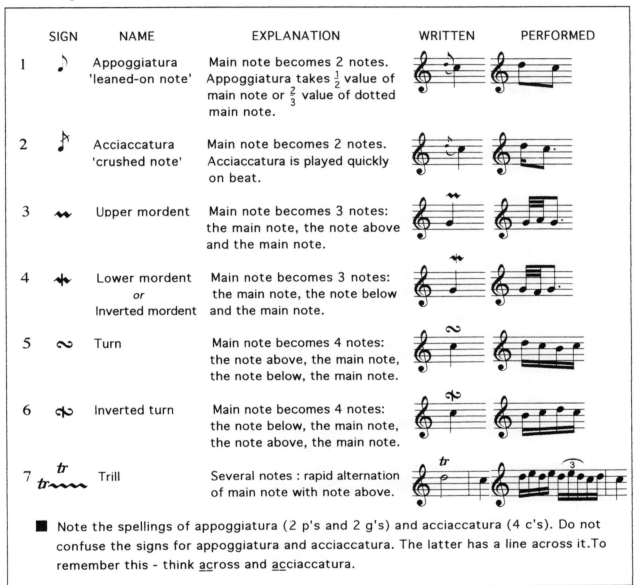

	SIGN	NAME	EXPLANATION	WRITTEN	PERFORMED
1		Appoggiatura 'leaned-on note'	Main note becomes 2 notes. Appoggiatura takes $\frac{1}{2}$ value of main note or $\frac{2}{3}$ value of dotted main note.		
2		Acciaccatura 'crushed note'	Main note becomes 2 notes. Acciaccatura is played quickly on beat.		
3		Upper mordent	Main note becomes 3 notes: the main note, the note above and the main note.		
4		Lower mordent *or* Inverted mordent	Main note becomes 3 notes: the main note, the note below and the main note.		
5		Turn	Main note becomes 4 notes: the note above, the main note, the note below, the main note.		
6		Inverted turn	Main note becomes 4 notes: the note below, the main note, the note above, the main note.		
7		Trill	Several notes : rapid alternation of main note with note above.		

■ Note the spellings of appoggiatura (2 p's and 2 g's) and acciaccatura (4 c's). Do not confuse the signs for appoggiatura and acciaccatura. The latter has a line across it. To remember this - think <u>ac</u>ross and <u>ac</u>ciaccatura.

Exercise 81 Identify the numbered ornaments in the following extracts :

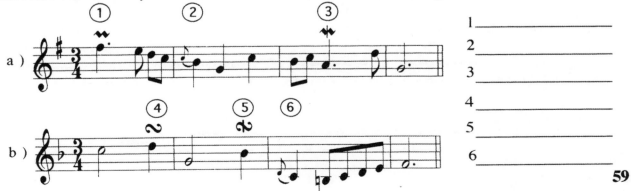

1 _____
2 _____
3 _____
4 _____
5 _____
6 _____

■ On pages 12 -14 and 41 explanations and exercises are given on writing word rhythms. Revise these pages.

● Up to now, one line of poetry has been matched by one line of rhythm. Where the next line of poetry had no anacrusis, the preceding line of rhythm ended with a bar line. Study this example (taken from page 12) which illustrates this point.

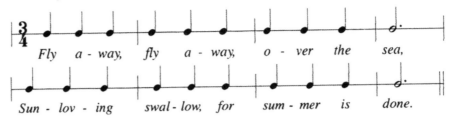

If the next line of poetry began with an anacrusis, the last bar of the preceding line was left without a bar line, i.e. it was incomplete. The next example shows this.

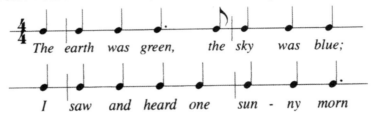

Because writing word rhythms is a preparation for writing songs, it is obvious that the bars should be as complete as possible. So from now on, the last bar of each line of rhythm will be <u>made complete</u> and include the up-beat to the next phrase. Examine the next example carefully.

First, study the stanza, noting where the accents are marked. Lines 2, 3 and 4 start with up-beats which are un-accented. Then, in the rhythm setting, note how these words (up-beats) have been included in the last bar of the preceding line.

> " Like the léaves of the forest when súmmer is green
> That hóst with their banners at súnset were seen;
> Like the léaves of the forest when áutumn hath blown,
> That hóst on the morrow lay wíther'd and brown."   Lord Byron

Exercise 82   Write a 4-phrase rhythm for each of the following stanzas. The first and last bar lines of each line are given.

a)

$\frac{4}{4}$ "There | was an old owl who lived in an oak ; The

| more he heard , the less he spoke. The

| less he spoke , the more he heard.

| Why aren't we like that wise old bird ? "   R.L.Stevenson

b)

$\frac{4}{4}$ "Far and few , far and few , Are the

| lands where the Jumb - lies live ; Their

| heads are green , and their hands are blue , And they

| went to sea in a sieve ."   Edward Lear

c)   "There lived an old man in the kingdom of Tess,
Who invented a purely original dress;
And when it was perfectly made and complete,
He opened a door and walked into the street."   Edward Lear

Just as there are augmented and diminished intervals, so there are augmented and diminished triads.

The **augmented triad** is obtained by taking a <u>major</u> triad and raising the 5th by a semitone. This turns the perfect 5th into an augmented 5th. The augmented triad therefore consists of a major 3rd and an augmented 5th.

major 3rd + perfect 5th = major triad   major 3rd + aug 5th = augmented triad

The **diminished triad** is obtained by taking a <u>minor</u> triad and lowering the 5th by a semitone. This turns the perfect 5th into a diminished 5th. The diminished triad therefore consists of a minor 3rd and a diminished 5th.

minor 3rd + perfect 5th = minor triad   minor 3rd + dim 5th = diminished triad

Augmented and diminished triads will be met with later in the study of keys and chords. For the moment it is sufficient to know how they are constructed.

Exercise 83   Turn these major triads into augmented triads. The first one has been done.

major   aug

Exercise 84   Turn these minor triads into diminished triads.

Exercise 85   Identify whether each triad is major, minor, augmented or diminished.

a)

b)

Exercise 86   Above each root note add a 3rd and a 5th to form the required triad.

augmented   minor   diminished   major   diminished   major   augmented   minor

SIGHT CLAPPING 4 : SYNCOPATION & JAZZ RHYTHMS

The feature that often strikes listeners first about jazz is its rhythm. Jazz is largely improvised music, that is, it is composed 'on the instant' and without preparation. Therefore the rhythmic language is subtle and often complex with syncopation an important ingredient. **Syncopation** stresses notes other than the main beats in a bar. This creates rhythmic tension and an element of surprise.

Frequently, syncopation is created by anticipating a main beat, i.e. playing it a little early. A simple rhythm such as $\frac{4}{4}$ ♩ ♩ can be transformed, if the third beat is played a half-beat early to become $\frac{4}{4}$ ♩. ♪♩

Characteristic jazz rhythms in $\frac{4}{4}$ tend to stress beats 2 and 4 and often anticipate beats 1 and 3 by a half-beat. For example:

Practise clapping these patterns. Feel the sense of the rhythm by moving with the pulse in an easy relaxed way. Begin slowly and increase speed as you gain confidence.

Exercise 87   Improvise 4-bar rhythms using combinations of the patterns clapped already.

Exercise 88   Clap the next rhythms *solo* or, better, practise with others as a group. If in a group, try having one half add an accompaniment. This makes the rhythms more interesting and challenging. It is important to listen carefully to one another so that the rhythms synchronise perfectly.

INSTRUMENTS and SPECIAL EFFECTS

■ The information here is a summary of an extensive topic covering the instruments of the orchestra, their sound, method of sound production and range. Refer to *Music Workout, Grade 5* and other resources in your school or other libraries.

● **Main orchestral instruments**

STRINGS   violin, viola, 'cello, double bass, harp

WOODWIND   flute, oboe, clarinet, bassoon
Each instrument of the woodwind group, has an occasionally-used related instrument which sounds lower than the main one, except for the flute.

     flute   piccolo (*flauto piccolo* = little flute): <u>higher</u> sound than flute
     oboe   cor anglais / English horn
     clarinet   bass clarinet
     bassoon   double bassoon

BRASS   horn, trumpet, trombone, tuba

PERCUSSION   timpani (kettle drums), side drums, bass drum, cymbals

● **Special Effects**   These terms and signs are used as 'performance directions' for certain instruments to tell how the music is to be played.

STRINGS   *pizzicato (pizz.)* = strings to be plucked.
            arco   = strings played with the bow. Used after pizzicato.
            ⊓   = play 'down' bow stroke.
            ⋁   = play 'up' bow stroke.
            ⌒   = play all notes under the slur with one bow stroke.
   con sordino or *con sord* = play with mute to give a hushed sound. A mute
                           for strings is a small clamp placed on the bridge.
       senza sordino = play without mute / remove the mute.
     glissando (harp) = play sliding sweep of fingers across the strings.

BRASS   *con sord*   = with mute; this produces a more distant sound.
                         A mute is a cone which is inserted into the bell.
        senza sord = remove the mute.

PIANO   *una corda* / 'one string' = press the left pedal.
     tre corde / 'three strings' = release the left pedal.

         𝄢ed.   ✳
                       = press / release the right pedal.
         𝄢ed. ———⌋

          ⦃   = spread chord notes, starting from the lowest note.

       m.s. = play with left hand / mano sinistra.
       m.d. = play with right hand / mano destra

GENERAL OBSERVATION 4

Study this extract from a piano sonata by Haydn. Then answer the questions below.

1. (a)   Name the key of bars 1 - 4. _____   Name the key of bars 6 - 8. _____

   (b)   Describe each of the marked intervals:

   W (bar 2) _____   X (bar 4) _____

   Y (bar 5)_____   Z (bar 6)_____

2. (i)   Explain **Vivace molto**. _____

   (ii)   Give the technical name for the first note. _____

   (iii) <u>Three</u> of these ornament types appear in the extract. Tick those present giving the number of a bar in which each occurs.

   appoggiatura ☐ bar _____   **acciaccatura** ☐ bar _____

   mordent ☐ bar_____   **turn** ☐ bar_____   **trill** ☐ bar _____

3. (i)   Identify each chord marked * as I, IV or V.   bar 9____   bar 15 ____

   (ii)   The last note of the right hand part in bar 5 is reprinted here. Rewrite it enharmonically.

   (iii) The first 4 notes of the right hand part are marked ⌐⎺ ⎺ ⎺ ⎺⌐. Mark in a similar way where this pattern is repeated a 2nd lower.

   (iv)   Bars 15 -18 repeat bars 1 - 4. State 3 differences between the original and the repeat.

   _____

   _____

   _____

Q.1(a) Identify the chords marked * as I , IV or V.

  (b) Rewrite the extract in open score. The first notes are given.

Q.2 Above each root note add a 3rd and a 5th to complete the required triad.

minor   major   diminished   augmented   major   diminished

Q.3 Complete a chord plan for each key. Write the indicated root position chords for S.A.T.B.

Q.4 Complete the following sentences about instruments.

The clarinet in B♭ belongs to the _____ family. It sounds a_____ lower than

written. The horn in F belongs to the _____ family. When written it appears

a_____ higher than it sounds. The_____ sounds an octave

higher than written. The_____ sounds an octave lower than written.

'General Observation' pieces are included in this and the earlier grades of *Music Workout* to show how theoretical knowledge can be used in a practical way. In these pieces the focus has been on <u>looking</u> at the music and then showing an understanding of it by answering questions. A next logical step is to <u>look and listen</u>, training the eye and ear to work in tandem to give a greater depth of musical understanding. It is for this purpose that the 'Aural / Visual Observation' pieces have been included. In them we focus on four aspects of the music:

1 Key   2 Time   3 Texture   4 Cadence

Key   To identify the tonic key <u>look</u> at the key signature and note the major and minor keys for which it stands. <u>Listen</u> to the sound of the piece - is it major or minor? If it sounds minor, confirm your answer by 'scouting' for the raised 7th accidental (*si*), the badge of the minor key. Also check the end - the piece is likely to finish on the tonic chord of the major or minor key. As well as naming the tonic key, you should be able to identify any note in the key by giving its technical name (tonic, supertonic etc.)

Time   Explain the printed time signature by stating if it is simple or compound, and whether it is duple, triple or quadruple.

Texture   The overall texture of most simple piano pieces is probably characterised by one of the following:

(a) Arpeggio or broken chord shapes.

(b) Melody with accompaniment. The melody may be in the treble or the bass.

(c) Chordal, i.e.using mostly block chords.

(d) Two strands of melody.

(e) Contrapuntal (from 'counterpoint'). This means that one part imitates another.

Cadence   A cadence is a musical 'punctuation mark' ; it will be sensed where the music 'takes a breath'. Some cadences sound like commas, while others give the effect of full stops. Later you will learn how chords are used at cadences, but the first step is to recognise the presence of a cadence by its <u>sound</u>.

Aural / Visual Observation Activity

On pages 68 -71 there are pieces and related questions for you to practise your observational skills. Ask a friend or your teacher to play each piece while you follow the music. It should be played through twice. Think about each question before giving a considered answer.

If you would like to check how you got on, you will find answers to each set of questions at the foot of page 75. Do not look them up beforehand!

Ask someone to play this piece through twice while you follow the music carefully. Then answer the questions below.

Question A (i) Name the key of the piece.

Name the relative of the tonic.

(ii) Is the time simple or compound?

Is it duple, triple or quadruple?

(iii) Give the technical name for each note marked with an asterisk in the bass part of bar 2 and bar 7.

Question B   Is the melodic interest mainly in the treble or the bass?

Question C   After a second hearing of the piece, give the number of a bar where you hear the effect of a cadence.

AURAL / VISUAL OBSERVATION B

Have someone play this piece twice while you follow the music. Then answer the questions.

Question A (i) Name the key of the piece.

Name another key with the same key signature.

(ii) Explain $\frac{6}{8}$ time : simple or compound

duple, triple or quadruple.

(iii) Give the technical name for each note marked * in bar 9 and bar 13.

Question B   Which term do you think best describes the texture of the music?

| melody with accompaniment | | chordal | | imitation between the parts |

Question C   When the piece is played again, identify a cadence point by giving the bar number in which it occurs.

AURAL / VISUAL OBSERVATION C

Have this piece played twice while you follow the music. Then answer the questions.

Question A (i) Name the key of the piece.

Name the relative key.

(ii) Explain $\frac{3}{2}$ time: simple or compound

duple, triple or quadruple.

(iii) Give the technical name for each note marked * in the treble part in bar 6 and in bar 7.

Question B   Which term do you think best describes the texture of the music?

| 2 melodic lines | | chordal | | melody with accompaniment |

Question C   When the piece is played again, give the number of a bar where you hear the effect of a cadence.

AURAL / VISUAL OBSERVATION D

Have this piece played twice while you follow the music. Then answer the questions.

Question A(i) Name the key of the piece.

Name another key with the same key signature.

(ii) Is the time simple or compound?

Is it duple, triple or quadruple?

(iii) Give the technical name for each note marked * in the treble part in bar 5 and in bar 6.

Question B   Which term do you think best describes the texture of the music?

| melody with accompaniment | | arpeggio figures | | chordal |

Question C   After a second hearing of the piece, name a bar where you consider there is a cadence point.

TEST A

Q.1 Identify the keys of these tonic triads and their triad position (root position, 1st inversion, 2nd inversion). Then rewrite each in open position.

Key _____ minor   Key _____ major   Key _____ minor

triad position_____   triad position _____   triad position_____

Q.2 Add a time signature. Then add a rest at each place where * is marked.

Q.3 Transpose this melody in B♭ major into the major key a minor 3rd higher.

" Bonnie Dundee "

Q.4 Name the keys indicated by these key signatures. Then draw the three primary triads in each key. Write roman numerals underneath.

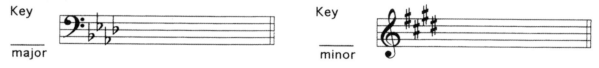

Key _____ major   Key _____ minor

Q.5 Finish this G minor tune to make 8 bars in all. Add phrasing, tempo and expression.

Rameau

Q.6 Write 3 different root position arrangements of each triad for S.A.T.B.

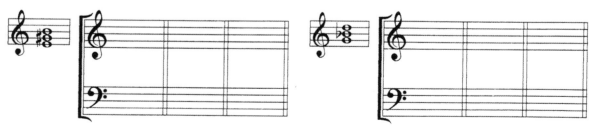

Q.7 Identify the ornament in each bar.

TEST B

Q.1 Add accidentals to make a harmonic chromatic scale beginning on B.

Q.2 (i) Describe each interval. (ii) Draw and name the inversion of each

_____ _____   _____ _____   _____ _____

Q.3 (i) Name the major key in which this melody is written. _____

Beethoven: Op.78

(ii) Transpose the melody down an octave, rewriting it on the given stave.

Q.4(a) Name the key of the extract. Write a chord plan. Identify each chord * with a roman numeral.

Key_____

Leipzig

(b) Rewrite the extract in open score.

S.

A.

T.

B.

Q.5 Fill in the blanks in the following paragraph.

The Baroque period covers the _____ century and the first half of the _____ . Three of the most important composers of the period were _____ , _____ and _____ . Two types of instrumental music they wrote were _____ and _____ .The orchestra started to evolve, consisting mainly of _____ instruments, with occasional use of _____ , _____ and percussion. A keyboard instrument, the _____ was also included. The main kinds of vocal music were _____ and _____ .

TEST C

Q.1 Write an octave ascending and descending of the scale of G♯ melodic minor. Use a key signature and necessary accidentals. Mark the semitones.

Q.2(a) This melody is in E minor. Give the technical names for the notes marked *.

Bach
etc.

_____ _____ _____ _____ _____

(b) Now transpose this melody into the minor key a major 3rd lower.

(c) Is $\frac{3}{8}$ time simple / compound?_____ Is it duple / triple / quadruple? _____

Q.3(a) Name the key of the extract. Write a chord plan on the short stave. Identify each chord marked * by giving its roman numeral.

Beethoven: Op.31 no.1

Key_____

(b) In bar 1 the group of notes marked '5' is a _____. It equals ___ beat(s).

Q.4 Write a rhythm for this stanza:

"The friendly cow, all red and white,
I love with all my heart;
She gives me cream with all her might
To eat with apple tart."

R.L.Stevenson

Q.5 Identify each triad type as major, minor, augmented or diminished.

_____   _____   _____   _____   _____

TABLES of KEY SIGNATURES

These diagrams chart the key signatures you have learnt so far.

Diagram 1

The white note is the tonic (*do*) of the major key.

The black note is the tonic (*la*) of the relative minor.

The small diamond-shaped note is the raised 7th of the minor key (*si*). This note always has an accidental which is not included in the key signature.

Diagram 2

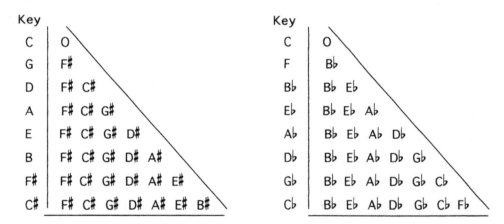

The order of sharps or flats reads the same horizontally and diagonally.

Sharps move up in <u>5ths</u> - a new sharp is the <u>7th</u> note of the key.

Flats move up in <u>4ths</u> - a new flat is the <u>4th</u> note of the key.

Answers   Aural/Visual Observation on pages 68 - 71

A : (a)(i) A minor ; C major   (ii) simple triple   (iii) leading note, mediant
　　(b) bass   (c) bar 8 or bar 12

B : (a)(i) G major ; E minor   (ii) compound duple   (iii) leading note, tonic
　　(b) imitation between the parts   (c) bars 4, 8 or 16

C : (a)(i) D minor ; F major   (ii) simple triple   (iii) dominant, supertonic
　　(b) chordal   (c) bars 4, 8, 12 or 16

D : (a)(i) D major ; B minor   (ii) simple quadruple   (iii) submediant, subdominant
　　(b) arpeggio figures   (c) bars 4, 8 or 15

HOMEWORK RECORD

DATE	